G GOSSIP
Whether it's the latest rumour or who's going out with who, it's *grrreat* to gossip!

H HOLIDAYS
When you don't have school, there's even more time for having fun. And holidays mean long lies, meeting friends and, best of all, no homework. Yippee!

I ICE RINK
Can you skate? If not, then pop along to your local rink and learn. If you already know how to skate, then see you at the Winter Olympics!

J JUGGLING
Juggling is great fun. Don't start with Mum's best fruit, though, try using thin scarves or small beanbags first. It's harder than it looks, but well impressive if you get it right.

K KITTENS
The cutest of the cute, that's cuddly kittens. They're just 'purr'fect and we *looooove* 'em!

her mate for lunch. Okay, so maybe that wasn't very funny, but you should try laughing, anyway. Laughter is good for you and a smile is **much** more attractive than a frown.

M MAKE-UP
Get together with mates and experiment with lots of different looks. It's great fun when there are a few of you.

Continued on page 78

Illustrations by Susannah Fishburne

Starscope

ARIES
(March 21 – April 20)
Don't let friends rule your life.
Lucky month: June
Lucky number: 5
Star birthday: Keira Knightley, March 26th

TAURUS
(April 21 – May 21)
There could be surprises at school.
Lucky month: October
Lucky number: 8
Star birthday: Andy Murray, May 15th

GEMINI
(May 22 – June 22)
A text or email might bring big news.
Lucky month: March
Lucky number: 7
Star birthday: Johnny Depp, June 9th

CANCER
(June 23 – July 23)
There's a gift coming your way. Weh-hey!
Lucky month: January
Lucky number: 2
Star birthday: Konnie Huq, July 17th

LEO
(July 24 – Aug 23)
A new hobby could prove lots of fun.
Lucky month: August
Lucky number: 11
Star birthday: Tina O'Brien, August 7th

VIRGO
(Aug 24 – Sep 23)
A holiday looks like bringing excitement.
Lucky month: November
Lucky number: 3
Star birthday: Billie Piper, September 22nd

SCORPIO
(Oct 24 – Nov 22)
Don't pay any attention to nasty gossip.
Lucky month: December
Lucky number: 10
Star birthday: Wayne Rooney, October 24th

SAGITTARIUS
(Nov 23 – Dec 22)
A party invitation could come at just the right time.
Lucky month: May
Lucky number: 6
Star birthday: Vanessa Hudgens, December 14th

LIBRA
(Sep 24 – Oct 23)
A friend has a secret to tell..
Lucky month: April
Lucky number: 9
Star birthday: Kate Winslet, October 5th

CAPRICORN
(Dec 23 – Jan 20)
A good turn could bring a reward.
Lucky month: February
Lucky number: 12
Star birthday: Orlando Bloom, January 13th

AQUARIUS
(Jan 21 – Feb 19)
A new friendship could be exciting.
Lucky month: September
Lucky number: 1
Star birthday: Cristiano Ronaldo, February 5th

PISCES
(Feb 20 – March 20)
Problems shared with a friend soon disappear.
Lucky month: July
Lucky number: 4
Star birthday: Dakota Fanning, February 23rd

p51

p7

p39

p5

p66

4

What's In?

p13

p26

p45

p32

p71

Some material may have been previously published.
Printed and published in Great Britain by D. C. THOMSON & CO., LTD., 185 Fleet Street,
London EC4A 2HS. © D. C. THOMSON & CO., LTD., 2008
ISBN 978 1 84535 350 6

Two's Company...

ALLY and Jo were looking forward to the end of the school term —

CAN'T WAIT [FOR?] THE CHRISTMAS [DANCE?] NEXT WEEK — [ESPE]CIALLY AS YOUR [BRO]THER SAM HAS [AS]KED ME TO GO WITH HIM.

I WISH I HAD A DATE, TOO, JO — BUT THE BOYS ARE PUT OFF BY MUM BEING THE TEMPORARY HEAD HERE.

YEAH. POOR YOU. BUT THINGS SHOULD GET BETTER SOON WHEN SHE MOVES TO HER NEW SCHOOL.

I HOPE SO. BUT I'M PRETTY SURE I'LL BE TAGGING ALONG WITH YOU TWO AGAIN NEXT WEEK. TALK ABOUT BEING A SPARE PART!

OH, I THINK WE'LL MANAGE TO PUT UP WITH YOU!

MAYBE — BUT REMEMBER, TWO'S COMPANY AND THREE'S A CROWD...

IT'S ALL VERY WELL FOR JO TO JOKE, BUT I FEEL A BIT LEFT OUT. JO'S THE ONLY REAL FRIEND I HAVE HERE, COS IT'S NOT JUST THE BOYS WHO AVOID ME. MOST OF THE GIRLS DON'T WANT TO BE FRIENDLY WITH THE HEAD'S DAUGHTER, EITHER.

10

10 Funky Facts about Miley Cyrus

She loves to nosh on Chinese food!

Miley was born on November 23, 1992, in Nashville, Tennessee.

Miley's godmother is the famous country singer, Dolly Parton.

She lists her favourite sport as cheerleading and her favourite hobby as shopping!

Her real name is Destiny Hope Cyrus. 'Miley' is a nickname and comes from 'smiley'.

She's best known as Miley Stewart in the smash hit TV programme *Hannah Montana*. Her real-life dad, country singer and actor Billy Ray Cyrus, plays her dad in the show.

She likes watching old movies like *Steel Magnolias*. Her favourite actress is Ashley Judd and her favourite singer is Kelly Clarkson.

Miley loves writing songs and some of her compositions have actually been used on her TV show.

Miley has been known to say, 'Pink isn't just a colour, it's an attitude'!

Her favourite song of all time is her dad's smash hit, *Achy Breaky Heart*.

HOW do you rate as a mate?

Are you the best friend ever – or really a bit of a rat? Try our fun quiz and find out!

1 Your friend has just got a new top — and it's exactly the style you were looking for. What are you likely to say?
a) I love it. I'm planning to buy one the same.
b) It's really nice. I'd like it in blue/pink/red.
c) Oh, I was going to get that.
d) Ha, ha, ha! You're not really going to wear it, are you?

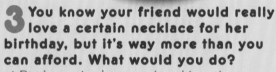

2 Your friend has been off school for two days. Would you...
b) Phone to find out what's wrong?
c) Think she'll be back tomorrow?
d) Ask someone else to sit beside you in class?
a) Call in to see her on your way home?

3 You know your friend would really love a certain necklace for her birthday, but it's way more than you can afford. What would you do?
a) Raid your bank account and buy it anyway.
d) You just give cards, not presents.
b) Get together with another friend and buy it between you.
c) Buy one that looks similar, but is half the price.

4 A girl at school says your friend has been talking about you. How would you react?
d) Stop speaking to your friend.
a) Cry and feel betrayed.
b) Tell the girl that you don't believe her. Your friend would never do that.
c) Rush to find your friend and ask her if it's true.

14

5 How many best friends have you had in your life?

a) Only one.
b) None. You've lots of friends, but no *best* friend.
c) One or two — depending on where you are.
d) Lots. You change your best friend every year.

8 The boy you secretly fancy asks you to give a note to your mate. Would you...

d) Take it, but 'lose' it accidentally on purpose?
a) Rush to give it to her right away?
c) Tell him to give it to her himself?
b) Be a bit disappointed but give it to her when you next meet up?

9 Have you ever passed on something a mate told you in confidence?

c) Well...if it was a really good bit of gossip you might be tempted.
d) Loads of times. You're useless at keeping secrets.
a) Never. And you never would.
b) Occasionally — but only to your mum or dad.

6 Your best friend asks you to help her with her maths homework. Would you...

b) Try to explain how it is done, then leave her to do it herself?
c) Say you will — if she writes your French essay?
a) Do it for her?
d) Think she should be able to work it out herself, so say you're busy?

7 She asks to borrow your new jeans to go with her new top. What are you most likely to say?

c) If you damage them, you'll have to buy me a new pair!
d) No. I'll probably be wearing them myself a week come next Thursday.
b) Fine — but take good care of them!
a) Okay. I'll go and get them now.

Illustrations by Wayne Thompson

10 Your old best friend comes back to the area. What would you do?

c) Meet her and your 'new' best friend on alternate nights.
d) Dump your new friend.
a) Take your old friend along every time you meet your new best mate.
b) Invite a whole lot of friends round and introduce her to them all.

Now add up your scores to discover your mate rating!

Mostly a
You're certainly a very loyal friend — but there is such a thing as being **too** close. Give your best friend a bit of space and accept that she might like to go places or do things without you always being around.

Mostly b
A near perfect best pal, that's you! You and your mate are really close — but you enjoy being on your own or with other friends or family at times, too. You're a well-balanced buddy and a great mate.

Mostly c
You're a pretty cool chum with a great mate rating. However, you tend to jump to conclusions quickly and find it difficult to trust people. Remember that your friend has a right to an opinion, too.

Mostly d
You come over as pretty selfish — but perhaps that's just a front to hide the fact that you feel insecure. Try to relax and realise that some people really want to be your friend.

Take Five!

Part 1

Five fabsy wordsearches — each with ten words hidden in it. Can you solve them all in five minutes? We hope not! Words can read up, down, backwards, forwards or diagonally, and letters can be used more than once. Oh, and you'll find *another* five if you turn to page 52!

Fruity fun!

Ten tasty fruits for you to trace.

- APPLE
- LEMON
- MELON
- PEACH
- PLUM
- BANANA
- MANGO
- ORANGE
- PEAR
- STRAWBERRY

S	S	N	Z	P	B	Y	O	G	P
P	T	F	O	A	G	G	H	U	E
E	W	R	N	M	N	V	N	O	A
G	W	A	A	A	E	S	G	R	R
N	N	A	M	W	M	L	N	A	H
A	K	P	M	P	B	K	L	M	C
R	L	P	N	O	L	E	M	G	A
O	E	L	O	N	G	U	R	G	E
H	O	E	E	C	X	I	M	R	P
J	L	G	G	W	K	J	H	Y	Y

Pets Corner!

Hunt for the hidden pets!

- BUDGIE
- CAT
- DOG
- GOLDFISH
- GUINEA PIG
- HAMSTER
- HORSE
- MOUSE
- RABBIT
- RAT

O	D	S	D	T	G	M	D	B	H
P	G	V	D	C	R	D	Y	U	S
R	U	R	S	T	V	P	O	D	I
G	I	P	A	E	N	I	U	G	F
Q	L	E	S	B	P	V	A	I	D
N	U	S	K	X	B	H	C	E	L
V	I	U	K	H	O	I	A	L	O
L	D	O	Q	R	R	A	T	I	G
H	A	M	S	T	E	R	A	A	Z
S	F	E	Q	C	E	C	U	O	M

16

Pick out
the pet pals!

©R.Kopfle/ardea.com

Country code!

You won't need a map
to find these countries!

- AUSTRALIA
- FRANCE
- ITALY
- NORWAY
- SPAIN
- CHINA
- GERMANY
- JAPAN
- PORTUGAL
- USA

B	L	E	C	N	A	R	F	A	Z
Y	K	A	F	W	N	C	U	N	E
A	N	P	Q	S	X	S	R	A	C
I	L	A	G	U	T	R	O	P	N
P	T	N	M	R	R	Y	H	A	A
A	R	A	A	R	A	R	O	J	B
E	T	L	L	W	E	U	V	C	F
X	I	C	R	Y	D	G	S	A	Z
A	K	O	N	I	A	P	S	U	E
A	N	I	H	C	R	U	A	E	G

Name game!

Is your name in the list below?

- ANGELA
- FEARNE
- KYLIE
- ORLA
- SUSANNAH
- CAROLINE
- HOLLY
- MEGAN
- RACHEL
- YOLANDE

E	A	Y	G	O	U	N	E	X	R
I	N	K	L	Y	R	N	H	A	E
L	G	Y	J	L	A	M	C	L	U
Y	E	L	O	N	O	H	A	R	M
E	W	I	G	L	E	H	U	O	G
N	L	E	N	L	A	Y	B	R	F
R	L	S	U	S	A	N	N	A	H
A	M	E	G	A	N	J	D	Z	E
E	C	A	R	O	L	I	N	E	U
F	O	V	R	J	T	K	T	V	J

Flower power!

Pick yourself a bunch of the best!

- BLUEBELL
- CROCUS
- DAISY
- ROSE
- SUNFLOWER
- CARNATION
- DAFFODIL
- LILY
- SNOWDROP
- TULIP

S	W	L	U	C	S	S	O	R	C
U	F	D	I	S	R	K	W	A	U
N	T	I	H	D	E	O	R	I	D
F	T	U	Y	D	O	N	C	A	R
L	U	P	O	L	A	F	I	U	O
O	L	G	N	T	I	S	F	C	S
W	I	Q	I	Y	Y	L	E	A	E
E	P	O	R	D	W	O	N	S	D
R	N	B	L	U	E	B	E	L	L
H	F	F	A	N	V	M	X	Z	P

So it was settled, except —

EVERYONE WILL KNOW FREDDY IS A BOY. AND WE'LL SOUND NOTHING LIKE THE BAND. WE'LL JUST LOOK STUPID.

NOT IF WE MIME TO THE SONG, ROZ.

YEAH. I WASN'T SUGGESTING WE ACTUALLY SING.

GEE, NOW I FOLLOW. IT'S A BRILLIANT IDEA, BECKY.

SO YOU'RE IN, ROZ?

SURE THING. WE CAN HAVE OUR FIRST REHEARSAL AT MY PLACE TOMORROW NIGHT. 'TWICE AS SPICY', HERE WE COME!

So —

WE'LL HAVE TO DO ONE OF THEIR EARLY SONGS — BEFORE GERI LEFT.

I HAVE AN EARLY ALBUM AND THERE'S A VIDEO, TOO.

COOL.

THIS IS AWESOME. WE CAN SEE ALL THE MOVES AND EVERYTHING. IT'S GONNA BE EASY.

AM I SPORTY, OR WHAT?

RIGHT, LET'S GET THINGS GOING. BECKY YOU STAND THERE AND LAURA THERE.

HANG ON, ROZ. WHO SAID YOU WERE IN CHARGE?

NOBODY. BUT I'M THE ONE WITH THE MOST DANCE EXPERIENCE.

I'M WITH LAURA ON THIS ONE. HOW CAN YOU DIRECT AND BE IN IT AT THE SAME TIME?

ACTUALLY, I'M DOING DRAMA AND DANCE. I'LL DIRECT IF YOU WANT.

Stancee, Roz's step-sister, had been watching.

So they took a vote —

ALL THOSE IN FAVOUR OF STANCEE.

LOOKS LIKE YOU'VE LOST OUT, ROZ.

SORRY, ROZ, BUT IT WILL BE BEST IF YOU CONCENTRATE ON BEING GINGER.

Rehearsals began in earnest —

THAT'S IT, FREDDY! THIS IS GONNA BE A KNOCKOUT, GANG.

Things were going really well, then —

AS SO MANY PEOPLE WANT TO TAKE PART IN THE CONCERT, WE WILL BE HOLDING AUDITIONS — X FACTOR STYLE. PLEASE WATCH THE NOTICE BOARD FOR MORE INFORMATION.

OH-OH. I DON'T LIKE THE SOUND OF THIS!

IT SAYS WE'LL HAVE TO PERFORM A SNIPPET OF OUR ACT IN FRONT OF A PANEL OF JUDGES.

AND THERE'LL BE NO COSTUMES, OR PROPS ALLOWED.

DOES — DOES THAT MEAN WE'LL HAVE TO SING THE SONG OURSELVES IN THE AUDITION?

YEP. LOOK, THE JUDGES ARE MISS LAKE AND MR MATTHEWS THE MUSIC AND DRAMA TEACHERS. BUT THERE WILL BE TWO PUPILS, AS WELL. THOSE INTERESTED HAVE TO PUT THEIR NAMES ON THIS LIST.

THAT'S NOT SO GOOD.

AND I BET THE FIRST TO PUT HER NAME DOWN IS JAYNE THE PAIN!

WE WON'T STAND A CHANCE IF SHE'S ON THE PANEL.

Sure enough —

QUITE FRANKLY, I THOUGHT YOUR ACT WAS PANTS. YOUR SINGING WAS AWFUL AND, UNLESS I'M VERY MUCH MISTAKEN, SCARY SPICE WAS *NEVER* A BOY!

I AGREE THE SINGING WASN'T GREAT . . .

23

They went down a storm —

MORE! MORE!

And, when the votes were counted —

AND THE WINNER — BY A LONG WAY — IS . . . 'TWICE AS SPICY'!

WELL DONE, ALL. THAT WAS JUST — JUST AMAZING!

THANKS TO YOU, TOO, STANCEE. YOU WERE A BETTER DIRECTOR THAN I COULD EVER HAVE BEEN.

WELL I STILL THINK IT WAS RUBBISH. YOU DIDN'T EVEN MIME WELL.

AND MY MUM SAYS THAT IT DOESN'T TAKE ANY TALENT AT ALL TO MIME TO SOMEONE ELSE SINGING!

D'YOU KNOW WHAT, MARGARET . . .

OUR MUMS SAY — WE DON'T CARE! PAL POWER FOR EVER!

The End

All about... Alex

A reader shares her secrets.

Hi! My name is Alex, and the thing I most like to do is read. As you can see, I have quite a collection of books. Jacqueline Wilson and Michael Mopurgo are two of my favourite authors, and I like stories that are based on real-life events. I've just finished a really good one about a girl who was caught up in the foot and mouth epidemic.

I also love baking — which makes me very popular with my little brother. The cakes shown on my computer are cup cakes which I made for his Cub party. I took a photograph of them and Mum helped me put it on a photo web site. We're both well into photography and Mum bought me a camera which is a smaller version of the one she uses.

When I went to my new school, I started having piano lessons — which I love. I'm also going to learn to play the viola (which is like a big violin).

As I am small, I will start learning on a violin that has been strung with viola strings. When I'm bigger I will be able to handle a real viola.

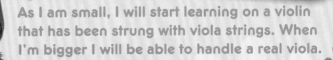

26

My favourite toys are my cuddly soft toys. I have a cool Bagpuss who can talk. I also love my Furby because he talks and sings silly songs. I like to sing along with him — but only when nobody is around! Like everyone else, I'd be lost without my Game Boy and my mobile phone.

I go to Guides, too. It's really good fun. And when I want to chill out I play games on my computer. It's in my bedroom, so my brother can't disturb me!

I love shopping for clothes. This top and green shrug cardigan are my best party clothes, but my favourite outfit is jeans and my new brown top.

Yes, this is really me! I'm dressed up in my special suit to help my dad look after our bees. We have to feed them and collect the honey, and it's a really interesting hobby. Each hive has a queen who lays the eggs, workers who go out and collect the nectar from the flowers, and drones who stay in the hive. They all have different jobs — but the end result is that they make me jars of lovely honey. Mmmm!

10 Funky Facts

about

The 'High School' guys

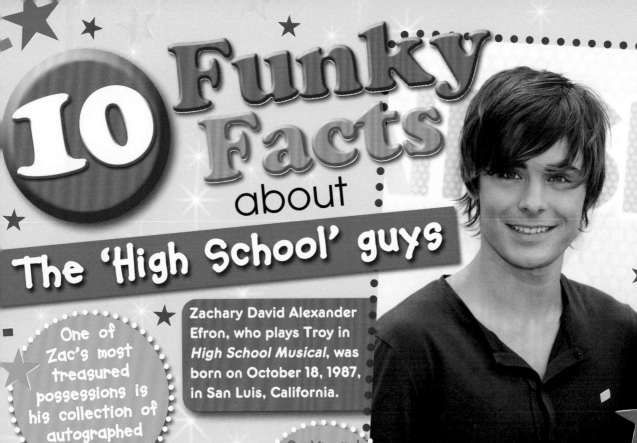

One of Zac's most treasured possessions is his collection of autographed baseballs.

Zachary David Alexander Efron, who plays Troy in *High School Musical*, was born on October 18, 1987, in San Luis, California.

Corbin and Zac went to the Football World Cup in Germany together.

For his performance in the hit 2007 film, *Hairspray*, Zac won a Young Hollywood Award.

Corbin Bleu stars as Chad in *HSM*, and he was born on February 21, 1989, in Brooklyn, New York. Bleu is actually his middle name and his real surname is Reivers.

Lucas, who appears as Ryan in *HSM*, was born in Springfield, Missouri, on the 23rd of November, 1984. His full name is Lucas Stephen Grabeel.

By the time he was four, Corbin was a professional model.

Lucas attended Kickapoo High School in Missouri — just like Brad Pitt!

Lucas used to play drums in his local Baptist Church.

When he was young, Corbin took ballet and jazz dance classes and was often the only boy!

We ♥ love elephants!

Three pages packed with all you ever wanted to know about one of our favourite animals!

© D Usher/ardea.com

ELEFUN!

What kind of elephants live at the North Pole?

Cool ones!

Which is which?

There are two main types of elephant – African and Asian. But how can you tell them apart? Read on and find out...

● African elephants have dipped backs and smooth foreheads.

● Asian elephants have arched backs and two bumps on their forehead. They also tend to be slightly hairier than the African variety.

● African elephants are the bigger of the two and can grow up to four metres tall. They also have larger ears, which are shaped a bit like Africa.

● Both male and female African elephants have long tusks. The female Asian has such small tusks we can hardly see them.

29 © T & P Leeson/ardea.com

Turn over for more fun and facts! ▶

Keep on trunking!

● An elephant's trunk is a combination of its nose and top lip. The trunk can do heavy work like moving logs — or delicate work like picking up a single leaf! An elephant uses its trunk to put food in its mouth and to suck up water, which it then blows into its mouth to drink. It can also use its trunk to shower itself with dust or cooling water, and to breathe when swimming underwater!

© J Rajput/ardea.com

● An elephant has a great sense of smell and sniffs the air by raising its trunk and swivelling it around. This way, the elephant can track friends, search out enemies and find its next meal!

● The trunk can also be used as a weapon. A flying trunk can pack a very powerful punch!

ELEFUN!
What do you get if you cross an elephant and a kangaroo? Holes all over Australia!

© Ferrero-Labat/ardea.com

● Elephants say 'hello' by entwining their trunks. They also use them to stroke one another, play games and attract attention. If an elephant raises its trunk, it's saying, 'Watch out!'. If it lowers its trunk, it's saying, 'Okay, you're the boss!'.

ELEFUN!
What's beautiful, grey and wears glass slippers? Cinderelephant!

● Calves are born nearly blind and use their trunks to feel their way about. They take a long time to get used to their trunk and can regularly trip over it!

Elefacts

- An elephant's tusks are in fact two of its upper teeth and can grow to over three metres in length!

- Elephants can live to over 70 years of age!

- Usually, working elephants are female. They are more easily trained and less violent than the males.

© M Watson/ardea.com

- An elephant's skin is about 2.5cm thick. But, round the mouth and inside the ears, it's paper-thin.

- Although Asian elephants are sometimes seen to lie down, African elephants rarely do unless they are sick.

- Elephants are the largest land animals living today!

ELEFUN!
Why can't elephants travel on planes? Because their trunks don't fit in the overhead lockers!

- Elephants can't trot, jump or gallop. They only have a walk and a fast walk – but can reach 24 miles per hour when moving at full speed!

- Elephants have the largest brains of any land animal and are very clever. They play, use tools, show kindness and love, mourn their dead, laugh and cry. They can even recognise themselves in a mirror!

© J Rajput/ardea.com

- An elephant is so massive it might have to spend up to 16 hours a day eating. They enjoy leaves, grass, twigs, roots, tree bark, fruit, seeds and flowers, and have been known to steal food from passing trucks!

- They are great swimmers! (And it's got nothing to do with them having trunks!)

- Mud protects an elephant's skin from the sun, insect bites and water loss. It also helps to keep them cool.

- Elephants have a great sense of hearing and listen using their ears, trunks and feet. They pick up noises from many miles away by placing their trunks on the ground and moving their sensitive feet to feel vibrations.

Create your very own Ele-friend

These cute little elephants are really easy to make.

1 With an adult's help, cut the milk container just above where the handle joins on to the main part of the container. Trim the 'handle' slightly shorter than the 'body'.

2 Make up some of the wallpaper paste as instructed on the packet, then tear the newspaper into strips of around 3cm wide by 15cm long and soak them in the paste. Use the strips to completely cover the outside of the milk container, overlapping to make sure there is no container showing. Leave it to dry for around one to two days.

3 For best results, repeat step 2, before covering the container with strips of white paper and paste in the same way. The white paper makes the 'elephant' much easier to paint.

4 When the white layer is dry, cut a short length of string for the tail, fraying the very end, and use the paper glue to stick it to the back of the elephant. Then fix the eyes in place.

5 Now it's time to paint the 'elephant' with grey or brown paint. Don't worry if it isn't perfectly smooth. After all, real elephants don't have smooth skin, do they?

6 Once the paint is dry, cut two ears from the egg box. The indentations where the eggs sit are ideal for this — although you may have to practise a bit until you get the shape you want. Paint the ears to match the body then attach them with paper glue.

7 Finally, stick the cocktail stick 'tusks' in place. There you have it — your very own ele-friend!

Strictly Dancing!

AS Danni Bond was leaving school one day —

THERE'S NAT WAITING FOR ME. WE'VE GOT ANOTHER PRACTICE TONIGHT.

HE'S GORGEOUS, DANNI. I WISH I HAD A GUY LIKE HIM WAITING AT THE SCHOOL GATES FOR ME.

BUT HE'S JUST A FRIEND, SARA. WE'RE STRICTLY DANCING PARTNERS, THAT'S ALL.

HI, DANNI. READY TO START THE NEW ROUTINE TONIGHT? IT SOUNDED REALLY EXCITING WHEN TONI TALKED US THROUGH IT.

YEAH. HARD, THOUGH.

Soon —

. . . AND UP! THAT'S GREAT. LOVELY LINES, YOU TWO.

Afterwards —

WELL DONE, BOTH OF YOU. I'M SURE YOU'RE GOING TO DO REALLY WELL IN THE COMPETITION.

THAT WAS BRILLIANT. I LOVE DANCING SO MUCH, AND SO DOES NAT.

YOU'RE LUCKY HAVING NAT AS A PARTNER, DANNI. I REALLY FANCY HIM. DON'T YOU?

I NEVER THINK OF HIM LIKE THAT, FIONA. IT'S STRICTLY DANCING, THAT'S ALL. WE'RE LIKE BROTHER AND SISTER, REALLY.

OKAY, DANNI? READY TO GO HOME?

SURE, NAT.

I SUPPOSE IT'S NATURAL THAT SOME PEOPLE THINK OF US AS BOYFRIEND AND GIRLFRIEND. WE SEEM TO SPEND MOST OF OUR FREE TIME TOGETHER.

Later, at home —

THERE'S A QUIZ IN HERE ABOUT THE TYPE OF BOY FOR YOU. I'LL READ OUT THE QUESTIONS AND YOU CAN ANSWER, DANNI.

OKAY, LORNA. FIRE AWAY. BUT I HAVEN'T REALLY GOT TIME FOR BOYFRIENDS, YOU KNOW. NOT WITH MY DANCING.

Soon —

. . . DARK HAIR, KIND EYES, THOUGHTFUL, ACTIVE, LIKES MUSIC. I DUNNO IF YOU REALISE IT, DANNI, BUT YOUR ANSWERS HAVE JUST DESCRIBED NAT. YOU *MUST* FANCY HIM!

HA, HA! I DON'T THINK SO, LORNA.

SHE'S RIGHT ABOUT MY ANSWERS, THOUGH. NAT *DOES* FIT MY IDEA OF A BOYFRIEND. BUT I DON'T THINK OF HIM LIKE THAT — DO I?

At their next practice —

HE IS GOOD-LOOKING, I CAN'T DENY THAT. AND HE'S A REALLY NICE PERSON . . .

MOVE YOUR ARMS LIKE THIS.

WE OFTEN HOLD HANDS, BUT NOW IT FEELS DIFFERENT. I THINK I'M STARTING TO SEE HIM AS A POSSIBLE BOYFRIEND.

GREAT! YOU REALLY LOOK AS THOUGH YOU'RE ENJOYING YOURSELVES.

I'M GOING TO ENJOY DANCING MORE THAN EVER NO[W] I'VE REALISED HOW FANTASTIC IT IS TO [BE] WITH NAT. I CAN HAR[DLY] WAIT FOR SATURDAY['S] COMPETITION.

On Saturday —

TOO EXCITED TO EAT? THAT'S NOT LIKE YOU, DANNI. WHAT'S SO SPECIAL ABOUT THIS COMPETITION?

OH, NOTHING, REALLY.

I'M LOOKING FORWARD TO BEING WITH NAT FOR THE WHOLE DAY — BUT I DON'T WANT ANYONE TO KNOW.

At the competition —

THAT WENT REALLY WELL. AND IT'S GREAT BEING WITH NAT. I WONDER IF HE FEELS THE SAME WAY ABOUT ME.

When the results were announced —

. . . AND IN SECOND PLACE, DANIELLE BOND AND NATHANIEL HARRIS!

COOL! THAT'S THE BEST WE'VE EVER DONE, NAT.

Then —

COME ON, NAT. HURRY UP, OR WE'LL BE LATE FOR THE PARTY.

MUST GO, DANNI — BUT I'LL SEE YOU AT REHEARSAL ON TUESDAY.

OH, I'D HOPED WE COULD GO SOMEWHERE TOGETHER. HE — HE CAN'T FEEL THE SAME WAY I DO.

On Tuesday —

I WAS THINKING THAT IT WOULD WORK WELL IF WE MOVED TO THE LEFT LIKE THIS AND THEN . . .

IT'S WONDERFUL WHEN HE PUTS HIS ARM AROUND ME. BUT I MUSTN'T BE SILLY. IT'S STRICTLY DANCING, TO HIM. NOTHING MORE.

The following Saturday —

HERE'S SOME MONEY, DANNI. HAVE A LOOK FOR SOME HAIR ACCESSORIES TO GO WITH YOUR NEW COSTUME.

THANKS, MUM. I KNOW EXACTLY WHAT I WANT.

So —

NOT BE MY PARTNER? BUT WHY, DANNI? WE'RE GREAT TOGETHER.

IT'S JUST THE WAY I FEEL, NAT. I — I DON'T WANT TO DANCE WITH YOU ANY MORE.

BUT, DANNI, I . . . OH, HI, ZOE.

I'LL SEE YOU AROUND, NAT. I'M SURE YOU'LL FIND ANOTHER PARTNER.

A few days later, at dance class —

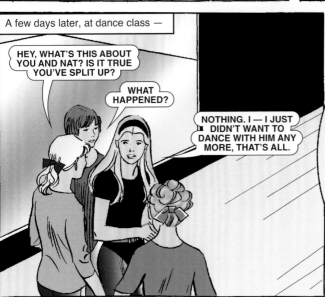

HEY, WHAT'S THIS ABOUT YOU AND NAT? IS IT TRUE YOU'VE SPLIT UP?

WHAT HAPPENED?

NOTHING. I — I JUST DIDN'T WANT TO DANCE WITH HIM ANY MORE, THAT'S ALL.

COME ON, DANNI. LOOSEN UP. YOU CAN DO BETTER THAN THIS.

I CAN'T. NOT WITHOUT NAT.

At the end of the class —

POOR DANNI. SHE'S NOT HALF AS GOOD A DANCER WITHOUT A PARTNER.

LYN'S RIGHT. BUT I'LL SHOW THEM. I'LL PUT IN EXTRA TRAINING AND GET UP TO STANDARD.

A week later —

I'LL START WITH MY WARM-UPS, THEN DO MORE WORK ON MY ROUTINE.

The new girl

by Susan Elizabeth Isaacs

"**C**OULD we have our ball back?" called a voice from the other side of the hedge. Lexi stood on tiptoe to see two girls standing on the other side. They both looked about her age and friendly, and both had brown hair — although one wore a pink band while the other had uneven-looking bunches.

Lexi picked up the ball and passed it over to the girl with the hair band.

"Are you one of our new neighbours?" the girl asked. "We saw the vans arrive."

"Yes," said Lexi, smiling shyly. "I'm Lexi. Do you live next door?"

"Petra does," said the girl with the bunches. "I'm her cousin Dawn and I live two streets away."

"It's great you're moving in," continued Petra. "The old couple before you made an enormous fuss if our ball went into their garden."

"Are you starting at St Catherine's School?" asked Dawn. "We go there and we're both going into Mrs Taylor's class."

"So am I," gasped Lexi. She'd been worrying about her new school, but now it didn't seem so bad.

"Why don't you come over and join us?" said Petra. "There's a hole in the hedge down in the corner. Crawl through!"

A few minutes later, after a quick call to her mum, Lexi was on the other side of the hedge, hearing all about the school cat, the grumpy caretaker, the nicest teachers and the ones it was best to avoid.

"It's a shame I'm off on holiday tomorrow — just when you arrive." Petra shrugged.

"But I'm around," said Dawn. "You can come over to my house. Give me your phone number, and I'll ring you."

Lexi was thrilled. She had only just moved in, and already she had two new friends!

She waited excitedly for Dawn to phone. But the next day came, and the next, and the next, and still Dawn didn't call.

Perhaps she never intended to, Lexi thought sadly. Perhaps she doesn't like me after all.

A week later, she mentioned it to her mum.

"Maybe she's been busy helping her mum and just forgot," said Mum. "Come to think of it," she added with a smile, "I seem to remember you promising something about weeding."

"Ah, but that was on condition that you took me into town to look round the shops," grinned Lexi. "That was the deal."

So, later that day, they found themselves looking round dozens of shops, and a huge market selling almost everything. Lexi forgot all about Dawn as she and Mum searched through scarves, hair accessories, shoes and bags.

Then, in a shop in the main centre, Lexi looked up to see a familiar figure. It was Dawn. Lexi opened her mouth to speak, but the other girl turned away abruptly. Tears stung in the corners of Lexi's eyes. Dawn didn't want to be friends. That was crystal clear now.

Lexi spent the rest of the day out in the garden. As she pushed her spade into the flower beds, she asked herself the same questions over and over.

"Why doesn't she like me? What have I done wrong? Will Petra ignore me when she comes back?"

"You've done a great job on those weeds," said Mum as she came out with a cool drink. "In fact, I think you deserve an extra treat. How about a burger in town?"

Half an hour later, as she munched on her fries, Lexi began to cheer up. Perhaps Dawn hadn't seen her? Maybe that was it.

Then, as Lexi turned away from the counter with a second drink, she walked straight into a girl.

Illustrations by Susannah Fishburne

"Oh, no!" The girl shouted at Lexi as dark liquid splashed over her white shirt. "Now look what you've done! Idiot!" As the girl looked up, Lexi recognized her immediately. It was Dawn. And there was no way she couldn't see Lexi this time.

Lexi spent the rest of the evening in her bedroom, crying. Dawn didn't like her. The chances were she'd turn Petra against her – and then the rest of the class. School was going to be awful.

The next day Lexi was still miserable as she headed outside to finish the weeding. Then, five minutes later, she heard a voice from over the fence.

"Hi, Lexi. How are you settling in?" It was Petra back from holiday. She seemed friendly — but perhaps she hadn't spoken to Dawn yet.

"Have — have you seen Dawn since you got back?" Lexi asked nervously.

"No." said Petra. "We thought we'd leave it a day. After all, she only got out of hospital this morning."

"Hospital?" Lexi was shocked. "But I saw her twice yesterday. In a shop and then in a burger bar."

"You can't have," said Petra. "She was rushed into hospital with appendicitis last week."

"But I know I did," gasped Lexi. "And she totally ignored me. She . . ."

"That wouldn't be Dawn," smiled Petra. "That would be her sister Claire. She's a year and a half older, but they look very alike – almost like twins."

"Oh," said Lexi, almost crying with relief, "that explains everything. But poor Dawn. Is she okay?"

"She's doing brilliantly," said Petra. "Do you want to come when we go to see her tomorrow?"

Lexi nodded, too frightened to speak in case she burst into tears. It looked like the three of them were going to be great friends, after all!

The End

Puzzled!

Two pages of hot puzzles to keep you busy

Quick Crossie!

See how quickly you can solve this cool crossword.

Mother and son. See 7 across.

Another mother and son! See 18 across.

Across
1. Looking glass. (6)
4. Spaghetti, macaroni etc. (5)
7. Albert Square soap. (10)
8. Rip. (4)
9. Joined links make one of these. (5)
11. If it's yours, it's … ….. (3, 4)
13. Mouse-like noises. (7)
15. Scorches. (5)
17. Take care of. (4)
18. ITV's Street. (10)
20. She looks after children. (5)
21. Make smaller. (6)

Down
1. Meat from a sheep. (6)
2. Very loud noise. (4)
3. Comes back. (7)
4. A state of fear. (5)
5. Opposite of he. (3)
6. The crime of burning things. (5)
7. Christian spring festival. (6)
10. Rouse from sleep. (6)
12. Imaginary circle round the earth. (7)
14. Seat on a horse. (6)
15. Often served with eggs. (5)
16. Bright or cheerful. (5)
17. Informed. (4)
19. Move quickly on feet. (3)

All Mixed Up!

Match the TV soaps to their settings.

EastEnders

Coronation Street

Home and Away

Hollyoaks

Neighbours

Summer Bay

Chester

Erinsborough

Weatherfield

Walford

Blankety Blank!

Fill in the missing words to find the titles of some classic TV progs.

1. Weakest _ _ _ _

2. I'm A _ _ _ _ _ _ _ _ _ Get Me Out Of _ _ _ _

3. The Vicar of _ _ _ _ _ _

4. Strictly Come _ _ _ _ _ _ _

5. Ready, Steady, _ _ _ _

Twice As Nice!

Score out the letters that appear more than once in each box to find three things we love!

1

L	E	F	R
A	W	S	W
E	H	R	I
O	L	N	E

2

A	F	G	C
P	A	R	I
E	G	N	P
C	D	A	S

3

O	P	N	B
A	N	R	M
M	T	O	I
B	E	M	S

Sharp Eyes!

Can you spot six differences between these two pics of the 'Bratz' girlies?

Movie Moments!

Unscramble the words below to find six of our favourite movies. Once you have finished, fit the names into the grid and the shaded squares will spell the name of a very well-known character. We've given you one letter to get you started.

- HRESK
- SRHIARPYA
- TZBAR
- HTE PSOMISNS
- TARATOLLEUI
- CANNY REDW

Does Springfield's first family feature here?

Answers

Quick Crossword! Across: 1 MIRROR, 4 PASTA, 7 EASTENDERS, 8 TEAR, 9 CHAIN, 11 NOT MINE, 13 SQUEAKS, 15 BURNS, 17 TEND, 18 CORONATION, 20 NANNY, 21 REDUCE. **Down:** 1 MUTTON, 2 ROAR, 3 RETURNS, 4 PANIC, 5 SHE, 6 ARSON, 7 EASTER, 10 AWAKEN, 12 EQUATOR, 14 SADDLE, 15 BACON, 16 SUNNY, 17 TOLD, 19 RUN. **All Mixed Up!** EASTENDERS/WALFORD, CORONATION STREET /WEATHERFIELD, HOME AND AWAY/SUMMER BAY, HOLLYOAKS/CHESTER, NEIGHBOURS/ERINSBOROUGH. **Blankety Blank!** 1 WEAKEST LINK, 2 I'M A CELEBRITY GET ME OUT OF HERE, 3 THE VICAR OF DIBLEY, 4 STRICTLY COME DANCING, 5 READY, STEADY, COOK. **Twice As Nice!** 1 FASHION, 2 FRIENDS, 3 PARTIES. **Sharp Eyes! SIX DIFFERENCES:** FROM LEFT: BRACELET FROM ARM, HAIR MISSING; LACE FROM DRESS; FINGER FROM WAVING HAND; EYEBROW MISSING; FLOWER ADDED TO BLACK DRESS; FLOWER MISSING FROM MIDDLE OF BROWN DRESS. **Movie Moments!** SHREK, NANCY DREW, HAIRSPRAY, THE SIMPSONS, RATATOUILLE, BRATZ. **The hidden character is** HARRY POTTER.

43

10 Funky Facts about

Ashley Tisdale

Ashley is best known for her roles as Sharpay in Disney's *High School Musical* films and Maddie in *The Suite Life of Zack & Cody* — where she plays a hotel clerk and babysitter to devious twin boys.

Ashley's middle name is Michelle, and she has one older sister, Jennifer, who also acts.

When she was only 12, Ashley sang at The White House — the home of the President of the United States!

She was born in Monmouth County, New Jersey, on July 2, 1985 — making her a carefree Cancer.

Ashley really likes reading and one of her favourite books is *The Great Gatsby*.

She also loves watching movies like *Just Married* and *My Best Friend's Wedding*. She lists Brittany Murphy and Julia Roberts as her favourite actresses.

Ashley isn't much into sport and says baseball is the only one she even slightly understands!

Her favourite colour is pink — and her favourite food is sushi. Her favourite time of year is Christmas.

Like most girlies, Ashley just loooooves shopping!

As a young child, Ashley was in a Broadway production of *Les Miserables*. Other stage appearances include *Annie*, *Gypsy* and *The Sound of Music*.

The Four Marys

MARY COTTER, Mary Field, Mary Radleigh and Mary Simpson were best friends at St Elmo's School for Girls. Christmas was approaching and the school was involved in all sorts of activities.

'. . . WE WISH YOU A MERRY CHRISTMAS, AND A HAPPY NEW YEAR.'

Next day, the girls were given a free afternoon to do some shopping.

WE WERE THINKING OF GETTING YOU A FRENCH PHRASE BOOK, COTTY?

HUH? WHAT WOULD I WANT WITH THAT, SIMPY?

YOU'LL NEED IT WHEN YOU WIN THE SCHOOL'S CHRISTMAS CARD COMPETITION. THE PRIZE IS A TRIP TO DISNEYLAND PARIS, REMEMBER.

FICTION

FOREIGN LANGUAGE DICTIONARIES

BUT LOTS OF PEOPLE WILL BE ENTERING. I . . .

BUT YOU'LL BE THE BEST. YOU'RE GREAT AT ART — ISN'T SHE, CAROL?

YEAH, SHE CERTAINLY IS, FIELDY.

BUT YOU'RE GOOD AT ART, TOO, CAROL. YOU COULD EASILY WIN THE TRIP TO PARIS.

I'LL CERTAINLY BE TRYING. I'VE NEVER BEEN ABROAD.

CAROL'S REALLY NICE, ISN'T SHE?

YES. BUT I HEARD THAT HER FAMILY HAS HIT HARD TIMES AND THEY'RE STRUGGLING TO KEEP HER AT ST ELMO'S.

BARGAIN CORNER HALF PRICE BOOKS

IT DOESN'T SEEM FAIR, DOES IT? MABEL AND VERONICA ALWAYS SEEM TO BE ROLLING IN CASH, AND THEY'RE SO HORRIBLE.

I AGREE WITH YOU THERE, RADDY.

Later —

COME ON, TIM.

I'D LIKE TO BUY THIS FOR MY MUM, BUT I DON'T HAVE ENOUGH UNLESS I USE MY BUS FARE AND WALK HOME.

47

THE STANDARD'S REALLY HIGH — BUT COTTY'S IS BEST.

YEAH, I RECKON IT'S THE CLEAR WINNER. IT'S REALLY ATMOSPHERIC. I LOVE THE PINK GLOW.

THAT'S CAROL'S. I'VE HEARD SOME OF THE OTHERS ADMIRING IT — BUT NOT AS MUCH AS COTTY'S, OF COURSE.

IT IS GOOD. BUT IT COULD BE BETTER. THERE'S SOMETHING JUST NOT QUITE RIGHT . . .

YEAH. YOU'RE AS GOOD AS ON THE PLANE ALREADY. SAY 'HI' TO MICKEY FOR US!

LEAVE IT OUT, FIELDY. I HAVEN'T WON YET.

AND I DON'T WANT TO. I WANT *CAROL* TO WIN.

I JUST WISH SHE'D SHOWN ME HER ENTRY BEFORE, BECAUSE I THINK I SEE HOW IT COULD BE IMPROVED. BUT IT'S TOO LATE NOW . . .

. . . OR IS IT?

Later that night —

YEAH, THAT MAKES *ALL* THE DIFFERENCE. NOW TO ALTER THIS ONE A BIT, TOO.

Home or away?

Follow our fun flowchart to discover your ideal holiday destination!

Start

Your idea of bliss is lazing by a pool for two weeks. True?

YES → **You own three or more different style swimsuits.**

NO → **You like activities such as tennis, cycling or walking.**

You own three or more different style swimsuits.

YES → **Trying lots of different foreign foods is great fun. True?**

NO → **You like showing off your French/Spanish/Italian.**

You like activities such as tennis, cycling or walking.

NO → **You like showing off your French/Spanish/Italian.**

YES → **You'd be happy to go to the same holiday spot every year.**

Trying lots of different foreign foods is great fun. True?

YES → **You often get travel sick.**

NO → **Airports are exciting, interesting places. True?**

You like showing off your French/Spanish/Italian.

YES → **Airports are exciting, interesting places. True?**

NO → **Airports are exciting, interesting places. True?**

You'd be happy to go to the same holiday spot every year.

NO → **Airports are exciting, interesting places. True?**

YES → **You like going somewhere with lots of arranged entertainment.**

You often get travel sick.

NO → **You don't mind where you go — Majorca or Mexico — so long as it's abroad and in the sun. Give you a villa or apartment with a pool and lots of sun beds and you're in holiday heaven.**

YES → **Travel's not really your thing, so a short flight, car or train journey suits you best. But whether you're in this country or abroad, you like living in a nice hotel with lots of people to look after you.**

Airports are exciting, interesting places. True?

YES → **You don't mind where you go — Majorca or Mexico — so long as it's abroad and in the sun. Give you a villa or apartment with a pool and lots of sun beds and you're in holiday heaven.**

NO → **Travel's not really your thing, so a short flight, car or train journey suits you best. But whether you're in this country or abroad, you like living in a nice hotel with lots of people to look after you.**

You like going somewhere with lots of arranged entertainment.

YES → **Travel's not really your thing, so a short flight, car or train journey suits you best. But whether you're in this country or abroad, you like living in a nice hotel with lots of people to look after you.**

NO → **Holidays at home are for you! A cottage in the country, a visit to an activity centre, or camping or caravaning. Loads to do and loads to see — that way you won't get bored!**

10 Funky Facts about

Emma Roberts

Her full name is Emma Rose Roberts and she was born in Rhinebeck, New York, on February 10, 1991.

She attended the Archer School for Girls in Los Angeles.

Emma comes from a showbiz family and one of her aunts is the mega-famous actress, Julia Roberts. **Wow!**

When she was only 9, Emma was in a movie with Johnny Depp. The film had an adult certificate, though, so her mum wouldn't let her see it!

Emma appeared as an extra in her Aunt Julia's hit movie, *American Sweethearts*.

One of Emma's favourite hobbies is reading, and her favourite colour is pink.

Emma sings and plays the guitar – talents which help her greatly with her role of Addie Singer in the smash Nickelodeon show *Unfabulous*.

Emma starred as teen detective *Nancy Drew* in the hit 2007 film of the same name.

In the movie *Aquamarine* Emma starred alongside JoJo and Sara Paxton.

Emma's performance in *Aquamarine* won her a Young Artist Award for Best Supporting Young Actress in a Feature Film.

Take Five!

Part 2

Five more wowsome wordsearches for you to puzzle over! Have fun — and remember that words can read backwards, forwards, up, down or diagonally and letters can be used more than once. Happy hunting!

A big hand for the Harry Potter lads — Rupert and Daniel

Cool collectables!

Collect these collectables!

- BADGES
- BOOKMARKS
- COINS
- DOLLS
- EARRINGS
- KEYRINGS
- POSTCARDS
- SHOES
- SOFT TOYS
- STAMPS

S	E	S	C	U	D	K	J	S	K
H	L	A	P	O	T	A	K	S	K
O	S	X	R	M	I	R	K	E	E
A	O	E	U	R	A	N	F	G	Y
P	F	P	O	M	I	T	S	D	R
S	T	O	K	H	A	N	S	A	I
G	T	O	L	L	S	V	G	B	N
P	O	S	T	C	A	R	D	S	G
B	Y	N	S	X	D	O	L	L	S
S	S	O	T	T	F	O	S	R	V

Groovy guys!

Track down ten of our fave lads.

- COLE
- DANIEL
- JOHNNY
- LUCAS
- RUPERT
- CORBIN
- DYLAN
- JUSTIN
- ORLANDO
- ZAC

I	Y	N	N	H	O	J	F	O	W
G	Z	K	Q	Z	K	N	P	J	O
F	N	G	Y	A	R	G	L	X	O
C	A	Z	N	U	N	E	G	L	D
J	D	D	P	I	I	N	U	B	N
U	J	E	T	N	B	C	O	Z	A
S	R	S	A	Z	A	R	U	D	L
T	U	D	T	S	E	L	O	C	R
I	O	J	E	H	D	U	Y	C	O
N	P	R	T	D	A	R	R	D	E

Subject matter!

Find ten school subjects and go to the top of the class!

- ART
- CHEMISTRY
- FRENCH
- HISTORY
- MUSIC
- BIOLOGY
- ENGLISH
- GEOGRAPHY
- MATHS
- TECHNOLOGY

Y	N	T	P	E	C	P	V	G	O
R	M	A	T	H	S	Z	B	E	W
O	R	I	S	U	M	I	F	O	W
T	E	C	H	N	O	L	O	G	Y
S	E	N	G	L	I	S	H	R	A
I	H	O	O	M	E	A	C	A	F
H	L	G	B	U	L	A	N	P	V
Z	Y	R	T	S	I	M	E	H	C
H	C	N	E	I	F	S	R	Y	A
G	N	A	C	C	A	O	F	T	P

Super sports!

Search for the hidden sports!

- ATHLETICS
- CRICKET
- DIVING
- HOCKEY
- RUGBY
- BASEBALL
- DARTS
- FOOTBALL
- NETBALL
- SWIMMING

A	Q	P	F	Y	Q	P	N	P	C
Y	B	G	U	R	D	T	F	I	R
S	N	A	Y	E	K	C	O	H	I
N	W	E	S	P	G	L	O	S	C
S	C	I	T	E	L	H	T	A	K
K	L	H	M	B	B	R	B	S	E
S	G	W	H	M	A	A	A	D	T
T	F	Y	L	D	I	L	L	O	B
S	K	W	L	W	M	N	L	L	M
P	X	D	I	V	I	N	G	A	E

Best of Britain!

Ten local locations to locate.

- ABERDEEN
- BLACKPOOL
- CHESTER
- LONDON
- OXFORD
- BELFAST
- CARDIFF
- EDINBURGH
- LUTON
- YORK

B	T	T	S	A	F	L	E	B	H
L	C	D	K	H	B	E	L	G	F
A	N	R	D	O	M	A	R	F	S
K	R	O	Y	Y	C	U	I	J	H
P	X	F	D	K	B	D	U	D	L
O	Q	X	P	N	R	G	D	R	U
O	A	O	I	A	O	X	U	M	T
C	O	D	C	N	Z	L	H	R	O
L	E	A	B	E	R	D	E	E	N
P	C	H	E	S	T	E	R	S	D

Are you really like your star sign?

Try our fun quiz to find out if you're positively Pisces or just a little bit Libra!

1 What are your favourite subjects at school?
a. Clever stuff like maths or science.
b. Needlework, cookery, woodwork or metalwork — creative, inventive, yet practical.
c. English or history — something with a good story.
d. Imaginative stuff like art or drama.

2 What's your favourite sport?
b. Anything — as long as people play fair and don't throw a strop if they lose.
c. You've no favourite — you shine at everything.
d. Anything that gets you in or near water.
a. Team activities like netball, football or rounders.

3 Would you like to be on the stage?
a. Yes! You love an audience and have a great memory for lines.
d. No. You love films and plays, but having to learn lines sounds a bit like hard work.
c. Of course you would! After all, you're a star and what better place to shine?
b. Not really. You'd hate all the attention.

4 It's your birthday. Do you throw a party?
c. Definitely — you love to dress up and surround yourself with admiring mates.
d. You'd rather watch a DVD with a couple of friends.
a. Yes — it's a great chance to catch up on the gossip.
b. Perhaps — you'd see how you felt on the day.

5 How would your friends describe you?
c. Enthusiastic, noisy — and fun, fun, fun!
b. Quiet, serious and reliable.
d. A daydreamer in a world of your own.
a. Clever, talkative, friendly.

8 What's your fashion style?

d. Smart casual wear is your thing — nothing scruffy or bright.

a. Girly outfits — mini-skirts, smart shoes, make-up.

b. You like comfy, practical stuff — T-shirts, tracksuits and trainers.

c. You love glitz and glitter — stuff to make you stand out from the crowd!

9 Where would you ideally like to live?

d. By sea, lake or river — near water!

b. In the peace of the countryside, surrounded by trees, flowers and animals.

c. In town where you can reach all the shops.

a. In a busy city where you can meet plenty of people and be involved in all the action.

Illustrations by Wayne Thompson

6 What do you watch on TV?

b. Practical stuff like how to buy a house, decorate a room or cook a meal.

c. You adore soppy love stories, historical dramas and murders.

a. Documentaries on science, history or nature.

d. Witches, aliens, ghosts, vampires, werewolves etc. Monsters are your thing!

7 Do you think of yourself as being romantic?

d. Yes, but you'd feel stupid if anyone found out.

a. Not really — but boys are a lot of fun and you'd love to date.

b. Not really — but a boyfriend might come in useful now and then.

c. Falling in love is your favourite hobby!

10 What would be your ideal job?

b. Cook, dressmaker, gardener, social worker, nurse or counsellor — something practical and caring.

a. Telephonist, chat show host, receptionist, police officer, teacher — you're a real people person.

c. Actress, singer, presenter, dancer or model — you're a born entertainer.

d. Artist, writer, poet, lyricist, composer, designer — you're imaginative and creative.

Now check out your answers!

Mostly a
You are most like one of the Air Signs — Gemini, Aquarius and Libra. You're intelligent, chatty, exploding with energy and ideas — a human tornado in fact!

Mostly b
Chances are you belong to an Earth Sign — Virgo, Capricorn or Taurus. You're known as being practical, reliable and sensible — and a great organizer, too!

Mostly c
You could well belong to one of the Fire Signs such as Sagittarius, Aries and Leo. You're flamboyant, colourful and energetic — shining like the sun!

Mostly d
Water Signs of Cancer, Pisces and Scorpio are the signs you're most like. Gentle, emotional and imaginative — you're the special child of the universe!

10 Funky Facts about

Dylan and Cole Sprouse

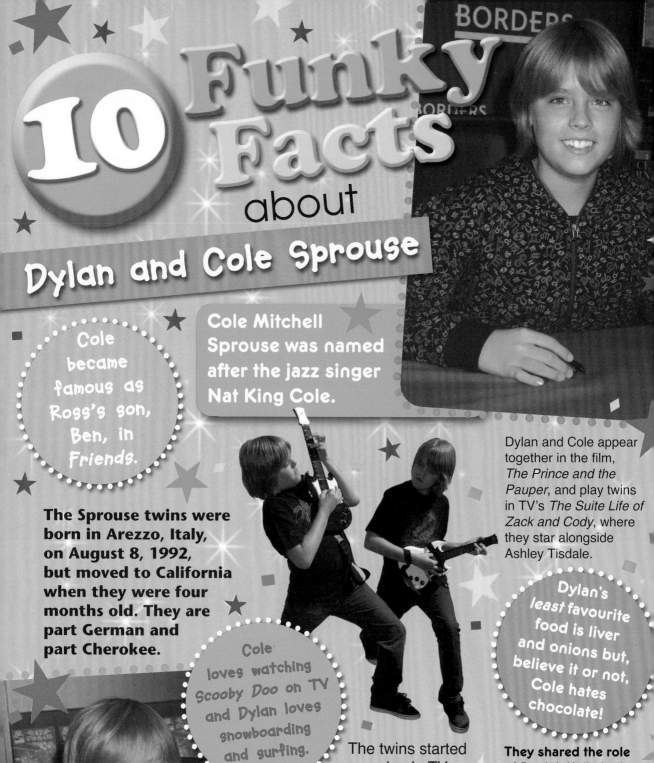

Cole Mitchell Sprouse was named after the jazz singer Nat King Cole.

Cole became famous as Ross's son, Ben, in Friends.

The Sprouse twins were born in Arezzo, Italy, on August 8, 1992, but moved to California when they were four months old. They are part German and part Cherokee.

Dylan and Cole appear together in the film, The Prince and the Pauper, and play twins in TV's The Suite Life of Zack and Cody, where they star alongside Ashley Tisdale.

Dylan's least favourite food is liver and onions but, believe it or not, Cole hates chocolate!

Cole loves watching Scooby Doo on TV and Dylan loves snowboarding and surfing.

The twins started appearing in TV commercials when they were six months old.

They shared the role of Patrick Kelly in the hit US TV comedy Grace Under Fire.

Dylan Thomas Sprouse, who was named after a famous Welsh poet and writer, is 15 minutes older than his brother.

Unlike Cole, Dylan doesn't want to continue with his acting. He wants to become a zoologist.

Carly's Cats!

CARLY COLLINS loved cats, and spent all her spare time helping at the Cat Sanctuary near her home.

YOU'RE A WONDERFUL AUNTIE TO ABANDONED KITTENS, MAISIE. WHAT WOULD WE DO WITHOUT YOU?

OH, SOMEONE'S AT THE DOOR. HERE, MAISIE. GIVE THESE KITTENS A WASH WHILE I SEE WHAT HE WANTS.

I'M HERE TO SEE THE MANAGER, MRS LAWSON. AND COULD YOU KEEP THESE ANIMALS AWAY FROM ME? I'M NOT VERY FOND OF CATS.

OH, WELL YOU COULDN'T WORK HERE. AND MAISIE'S JUST BEING FRIENDLY. FOLLOW ME.

THANKS, CARLY. YOU CARRY ON WITH THE KITTENS WHILE I SEE WHAT THIS CHAP WANTS. THEN WE'LL TACKLE THE WILD BUNCH IN THE SHED — SEE IF WE CAN GET THEM TO ACCEPT SOME HANDLING.

RIGHT, MRS LAWSON. AND I'LL GIVE THE INDOOR CATS THEIR MORNING MILK.

But a little later —

I'M AFRAID THAT VISITOR BROUGHT BAD NEWS, CARLY. OUR LEASE IS ABOUT TO RUN OUT. WE HAVE TO GO, CATS AND ALL, BY THE END OF THE MONTH.

BUT — BUT THAT'S TERRIBLE, MRS LAWSON. WHAT WILL HAPPEN TO THE CATS?

57

The next day Carly collected Tang from the vet, then —

TANG!

OH, NO! I DIDN'T FASTEN THE STRAP PROPERLY. IF HE PANICS I'LL NEVER CATCH HIM!

TANG, COME BACK!

HE'S GONE IN THAT WINDOW. I HOPE HE DOESN'T CAUSE ANY DAMAGE. THE SANCTUARY'S IN ENOUGH TROUBLE ALREADY.

TANG!

But —

OH — YOU'VE GOT HIM! SORRY, HE GOT OUT OF HIS BASKET.

SO HE BELONGS TO YOU? I WAS HOPING HE WAS A STRAY. IT WAS LIKE A SCENE FROM ONE OF MY OWN STORIES. HE CAME IN THROUGH THE WINDOW AND JUMPED STRAIGHT ON TOP OF MY COMPUTER — JUST AS MY OLD CAT USED TO.

YOU MEAN, YOU REALLY WANT A CAT? TANG'S LAME, BUT HE REALLY NEEDS A HOME. TANG AND I CAN BOTH SEE YOU'RE A CAT PERSON. WOULD YOU LIKE TO HAVE HIM?

I'D LOVE IT! I'VE HARDLY BEEN ABLE TO WRITE SINCE JASON WAS RUN OVER. CATS ARE GREAT COMPANIONS.

Then, as Carly headed for home —

CARLY — GUESS WHAT! I WAS GOING TO DO A BIT OF FISHING IN THE CANAL, AND I SAW THIS COUPLE ON A BARGE CHASE A RAT OFF THEIR BOAT. WE GOT TALKING — AND THEY SAID THEY'LL TAKE THREE OF OUR WILDER YOUNG CATS. THEY DON'T MIND COPING WITH THEM.

THAT'S GREAT, JAMES. AND TANG'S FOUND A HOME AS WELL.

But, as time passed —

I'M AFRAID I'M LOSING HOPE, CARLY. THERE JUST AREN'T ANY MORE PEOPLE WANTING THE OLDER CATS AT THE MOMENT.

I KNOW, MRS LAWSON, BUT — BUT THERE MUST BE SOME WAY WE CAN SAVE THEM.

A few minutes later —

NOW WHERE IS MAISIE? I HOPE SHE HASN'T GONE NEXT DOOR AGAIN — WE CAN DO WITHOUT MORE HASSLE FROM MRS HATTON-HALL. WILL YOU GO AND LOOK, CARLY?

SURE. MAISIE'S PROBABLY HUNTING ROUND THE OUTBUILDINGS AGAIN.

MAISIE! PUSS, PUSS!

I CAN'T SEE HER ANYWHERE.

Then —

THERE YOU ARE, MAISIE. HAVING FUN IN MRS HATTON-HALL'S PATCH OF CATMINT. OH, WHAT'S THAT SMOKE?

MRS HATTON-HALL! SOMETHING'S ON FIRE. MRS HATTON-HALL.

HER CAR'S THERE, SO SHE MUST BE INSIDE. WHY DOESN'T SHE ANSWER?

MRS HATTON-HALL — ARE YOU THERE? MASIE! WHERE YOU GOING?

62

All about...
Amelia

Another reader tells all!

Hi. My name is Amelia and these are some of my fortune telling books and cards. I like all kinds of fortune telling — from tarot cards to reading palms — and I've got lots of books on the subject.

I've been going to drama school on a Thursday ever since I was 4 or 5. Acting is my favourite hobby and I was delighted when I was voted Best Comedy Actress and was presented with this trophy. Through my drama school I've been in several TV programmes. I played Chelsea in *The Revenge Files of Alistair Fury*, and I was also in *Rocket Man* and *Wire In the Blood*. Acting can be hard work — but I love it and it feels really good when you see yourself on TV.

At drama we do mime and voice training as well as acting, and I have my own microphone so I can practice singing at home. I won a singing competition at my old school and I've sung on a TV ad for fish. I also auditioned for *Britain's Got Talent* — which was exciting. I'm wearing my favourite dress in this picture. I got it when I was a bridesmaid for my auntie. She let me choose it myself. I used to do dancing and ice-skating, but I don't have time now as I have so many other hobbies.

When I'm not acting or singing I like swimming and scuba diving. A friend's dad has a diving club and we use the pool at a school near us. I also like reading. It's really relaxing.

These are some of my bags. I'd love to collect more because they're really cool!

I like dressing up and doing my hair — which is just as well, as I have to do a lot of that when I'm acting.

How do you like my Betty Boop? She's my favourite cartoon character and Mum saw the figure in a shop window when we were in a taxi in London. She jumped out and got it for me because I collect lots of Betty Boop things. I've even got red, 'Betty' style shoes.

Snakes 'n' Ladders

Loads of word fun for puzzle fans! Complete the ladders by changing the words one letter at a time in the number of steps shown — making a new word every time.

Use the clues to fill in the missing words in the snakes, remembering that each word begins with the last letter of the word before.

When you have finished, you can rearrange the letters in the yellow squares to find a word related to each theme. Have fun!

Animal Antics!

CLUES

1. Jumbo animal.
2. Big stripey cat.
3. Rhino for short.
4. Smelly little animal.
5. Australian hopper.
6. Rhymes with water.
7. Bunny.

Hidden word:
King of the jungle

SNAP

TWIG

POST

CARD

BOOT

SHOE

CLUES — Just Capital!

1. Capital of France.
2. Capital of Sweden.
3. Capital of Spain.
4. Capital of Ireland.
5. Capital of Cyprus.

Hidden word:
Nordic capital

HAND

FOOT

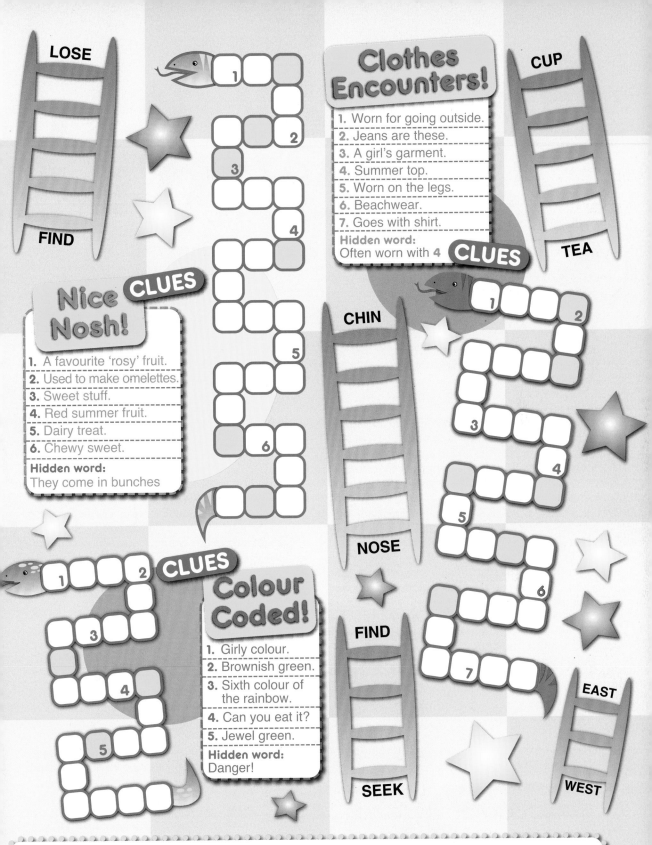

LOSE

FIND

Clothes Encounters!

1. Worn for going outside.
2. Jeans are these.
3. A girl's garment.
4. Summer top.
5. Worn on the legs.
6. Beachwear.
7. Goes with shirt.

Hidden word:
Often worn with 4

CUP

TEA

CLUES

Nice Nosh!

CLUES

1. A favourite 'rosy' fruit.
2. Used to make omelettes.
3. Sweet stuff.
4. Red summer fruit.
5. Dairy treat.
6. Chewy sweet.

Hidden word:
They come in bunches

CHIN

NOSE

FIND

SEEK

EAST

WEST

CLUES

Colour Coded!

1. Girly colour.
2. Brownish green.
3. Sixth colour of the rainbow.
4. Can you eat it?
5. Jewel green.

Hidden word:
Danger!

Answers

67

Suzy plays a trick

by Tracy Joy Holroyd

SUZY stood centre stage and gazed into the darkened auditorium. Her eyes scanned the rows of empty seats, the wide aisles, the ornate boxes, the dark recesses of the balcony.

"This place is so cool," she shouted.

Her friend, Amy, wandered from behind the heavy, tattered velvet curtains where the rest of the group was exploring the backstage area, and turned up her nose.

"Old and smelly, more like," she said. "It gives me the creeps."

"Me, too," agreed Suzy. "But that's why I love it."

"They say it's haunted," Amy added. "Over a hundred years ago one of the actresses threw herself over the balcony. People say they've seen her up there, watching rehearsals – all grey and twisted."

"That's horrible!" The girls spun around as the stage curtains opened, exposing the rest of their drama group – three girls, three boys and the teacher, Kath. "You shouldn't scare people with silly stories like that," Kath said firmly. "I can assure you that I've been in this theatre lots of times and I've never yet seen a ghost."

"Well, if I see anything spooky lurking up in the balcony, I'll just die!" Ruth's voice quivered as she gazed firmly at the floor.

Suzy narrowed her eyes and smiled.

"It's cruel!" Amy shrieked, giggling.

"But it's fun!" Suzy replied.

"I'll dress up in black and paint my face all grey and horrible, then stand on the balcony. There'll be just enough light for everyone to see me. You'll be down on stage, so you can pretend to notice me and point me out to everyone! They'll be terrified."

"They'll know it's you when they realise you're missing," Amy said.

"But not before I've given them a real fright!"

"It'd be a laugh, I suppose," Amy grinned.

"This Saturday, then?"

"This Saturday," Amy nodded.

"Great rehearsal," Kath yelled as she jumped up onto the stage. "Take a five minute break."

The kids moved together and started opening crisp packets and popping cans of fizzy drinks. Suzy looked at her watch. Time. She swapped a knowing glance with Amy, who was just settling down with a can of Coke, then nodded. Amy returned the nod, then turned to Jane and started chatting.

Suzy stepped quietly backstage, then made her way to the toilets where she'd left her outfit and make-up. She could feel her heart beating in her chest. This was almost as good as opening night!

She worked quickly, slipping on a black taffeta dress with high ruffled neck and long, full sleeves. She painted her face grey, drew dark shadows under her eyes and in the hollows of her cheeks and put on an old-fashioned bonnet. She regarded herself in the mirror and smiled. She looked awful. Exactly as she had hoped.

Quietly she opened the balcony door, slipped into the aisle and down the steps to the front row. She crouched to remain unseen and edged her way to the centre. There, she straightened and stood quietly with folded hands.

The people on stage were all focussed on Kath. Pete and Dave were sitting cross-legged on the floor, Ruth, Stacy and Tom on the sofa behind them. Amy was still sitting on a box next to Jane. Her eyes kept flicking up to the balcony.

68

Illustrations by Susannah Fishburne

Suddenly, she looked straight at Suzy, then her eyes widened and her face slowly drained of colour. It took Suzy all her strength not to laugh – what a performance! She knew Amy could act – but she should win an Oscar for this!

Amy slowly lifted a shaking arm and pointed.

"Look . . ." she whispered hoarsely. "Look . . . "

Everyone turned to gaze up at Suzy — and froze. Slowly, all eyes opened with horror, mouths gaped and faces blanched. Then Ruth screamed and everyone leapt to their feet.

"Which one of us is up there?" Kath shouted.

"It's Suzy." Jane glanced around. "Someone get up there, quickly!"

Pete, Tom and Dave dashed down into the auditorium and started running towards the stairs.

Suzy gasped. She hadn't expected such a panic. She'd expected people to scream – then laugh. She had to get out and calm everyone down.

Stumbling, she pulled up her long skirts then, heart pounding, she ran towards the stairs that led into the theatre lobby – just as the boys burst through the doors.

"Suzy! Suzy!" Pete yelled, his voice shrill. "Suzy, are you all right?"

"Of course, I am," Suzy replied. "It was just a silly joke. I thought you'd know it was me."

"Of course we knew it was you!" Tom gasped.

"So what was everyone screaming at?" Suzy snapped, seriously unnerved.

"The ghastly creature that was standing right behind you." Dave's eyes filled with terror. "It was all grey and twisted. The most horrible thing I've ever seen in my life!" **The End**

Chill out!

Loadsa cool facts about our fave feathered friends.

Wish I'd worn my cosy babygrow...

- **Although penguins are birds, they cannot fly.**

  - The only time penguins are airborne is when they leap out of the water.

- **Penguins like to slide across the ice on their big stomachs.**

  Most people think that penguins only live in Antarctica and other cold places, but some penguins live in much warmer climates, such as the Galapagos Islands near the equator.

Wheeeee!!! Anyone for a tummy slide?
© G Robertson/Ardea.com

- There are 17 different species of penguins — Adelie, African, Chinstrap, Emperor, Erect Crested, Fiordland, Galapagos, Gentoo, Humboldt, King, Little (or Blue), Macaroni, Magellanic, Rockhopper, Royal, Snares and Yellow Eyed.

- Penguins communicate with each other using movements and sounds. In that way they can warn each other if they sense danger.

- **Penguins cannot breathe underwater, but they are able to hold their breath for a long time.**

  Most penguins share the parental duties of caring for the egg, but the Emperor male has to do it on his own for up to nine weeks. He keeps it warm under a furry flap above his feet.

Emperor dads on egg-watch duty.

- **Penguins' wings are waterproof, which helps them to move through the water. They swim gracefully, almost as if they're flying.**

Wild hairstyle, Mr Rockhopper!

Penguins spend about 75% of their lives in water.

© G Robertson/ardea.com

Snares penguins, which live in New Zealand, have been known to roost in low trees.

© M Watson/ardea.com

Choices!

ANDREA was one of the top athletes in her school —

WELL DONE, ANDREA. THAT WAS YOUR BEST TIME YET.

AND I KNOW I CAN GO EVEN FASTER, MRS P. I'M DETERMINED TO MAKE IT TO THE COUNTY TRIALS THIS SEASON.

WELL, YOU'VE CERTAINLY GOT TALENT, ANDREA, SO ALL YOU NEED IS COMMITMENT AND DETERMINATION. IF YOU WORK HARD YOU COULD GO RIGHT TO THE TOP.

THANKS. IS THERE ANY CHANCE OF FITTING IN A FEW MORE TRAINING SESSIONS?

SATURDAY AFTERNOONS SUIT ME. AND IT WOULD BE GOOD IF WE COULD MEET UP SOME NIGHTS AFTER SCHOOL — EVEN FOR HALF AN HOUR. I'M NOT SURE WHEN I'LL BE FREE, BUT I COULD LET YOU KNOW TOMORROW.

I KNOW SOME OF MY FRIENDS THINK I'M DAFT, BUT I'LL BE THE ONE SMILING WHEN MY HARD WORK PAYS OFF AND I MAKE IT TO THE OLYMPICS.

NO PROBLEM. ATHLETICS IS MY LIFE, MRS P. I'D HAPPILY SPEND ALL DAY ON THE RUNNING TRACK!

77

The End

A to Z of things we like!

Part 2

N **NAILS**
Hunt out all your bottles of varnish and paint your fingernails or toenails — or both — the brighter the better. Try painting every finger a different colour. That's good for a laugh!

P **PARTIES**
Show what a great friend you are by organising a party for your best mate's next birthday. Oh, and remember to invite those boys you both fancy!

S **SCHOOL**
We might say we hate it, but we don't really. After all, that's where we get to meet our mates!

O **ORANGES**
The ultimate funky fruit tastes great, and is very good for us, too. Stick cloves in them at Christmas for original, sweet-smelling decorations.

Q **QUIZZES**
Get together with your bezzie and each make up a quiz all about yourself. Swap them over and find out how much you really know about each other.

R **READING**
Magazines, Harry Potter books, romances — and **BUNTY ANNUAL**, of course! Reading is a great way to pass the time.